EQUINE ACUPRESSURE

A Treatment Workbook

BY:

Nancy A. Zidonis
&
Marie K. Soderberg

EQUINE ACUPRESSURE
Winners Of The

SPRUCE MEADOWS EQUI  **FAIR**

1993 Award For Best Innovative New Service/Product

Edited By: Mickey Rubin
Cover Art and Illustrations By: Carla Stroh

Published By:	Equine Acupressure, Inc.
Printed By:	Parker Printing, Inc., Parker, Colorado
Copyright:	© 1991 by Equine Acupressure, Inc.

Library of Congress Catalog Card Number 90-859-69
ISBN 0-9645982-1-3

1st Edition 1991, 2nd Edition 1992
Printed in the United States of America
3rd Printing 1993, 4th Printing 1994, 5th Printing 1994
6th Printing 1995

To order **Equine Acupressure, A Treatment Workbook,**
write to:

> Equine Acupressure Incorporated
> P.O. Box 123
> Parker, Colorado 80134
> 303-841-7211

We are interested in your comments and suggestions regarding the material presented in this book as well as your experience with using acupressure. Please write to us at the above address.

This workbook is not a substitute for veterinary medicine. We suggest that you use acupressure in conjunction with your veterinarian's recommendations.

TABLE OF CONTENTS

1. FOREWORD

Most horseowners and competitors in equestrian sports spend an enormous amount of thought and time (and money as well!) trying first to maintain the health of their horse and second, to improve the performance of the horse. Owners, riders and trainers want their horses to feel better so they can perform better. And keep performing better.

In this workbook we describe treatment and exercises that further those goals. Developed by a massage therapist working in consultation with veterinarians, the acupressure treatments work to establish equine well-being by using

1) your relationship with the horse,
2) ancient Chinese medical principals,
3) and a holistic approach to therapy.

Our treatment program is drug-free and tailored to the needs of the horse. Some programs treat ill or injured horses. Others are directed at maintaining health or preventing injury.

While many people regard acupressure as exotic, it is an increasingly familiar part of the performance routines of many competitors. People whose livelihoods depend on the health of their horses rely on acupressure as a form of therapy.

Acupressure was part of the treatment used to help champion race mare Meadow Star recover from injuries. Endurance riders competing for the Tevis Cup use acupressure massage to relax their horses and restore stressed animals to normal condition. Linda Tellington-Jones made acupressure one of the cornerstones of her noted training method.

At Equine Acupressure, Inc., we found that acupressure massage and physical therapy could treat various common physical and behavioral problems. Our methods successfully remedied soreness, lameness, tendonitis, colic, founder, arthritic conditions and paralysis. We do not claim cures, we did see significant, lasting improvement in the condition of the horses we treated--even though conventional techniques had been tried and exhausted.

Such behavioral problems as cribbing, sour dispositions and hypersensitivity also responded to acupressure.

Acupressure treatment is not limited to a particular breed of horse or performance activity. Our patients have been Arabs, European Warmbloods, Thoroughbreds, Morgans, Quarter Horses and more. They have been hunter/jumpers, pleasure mounts, dressage horses, barrel racers and breeding stock.

As diverse as these horses were, as varied their problems, we were able to help them through acupressure massage. While this workbook is not a comprehensive treatment manual and acupressure is not a cure-all, we believe it can help you and your horse. Please remember always to consult your veterinarian in case of an illness or injury to your horse. If you work in partnership with your veterinarian, you will find that acupressure massage adds an important element to your horse's health care and performance routine.

2. INTRODUCTION TO ACUPRESSURE

Before you try acupressure with your horse, you should understand how it differs from the kind of treatment you are accustomed to applying. Here is a brief introduction to the history of acupressure and the philosophy behind it.

History

Acupressure is an ancient Oriental method of therapy used for a wide variety of human and animal disorders. First developed by the Chinese more than 3,000 years ago, it consists of pressure stimulation of precise points on the surface of the body. This approach differs significantly from Western medicine.

According to Western thought, health problems are caused by disease. Medicine, including veterinary science, diagnoses the disease underlying a given complaint and prescribes medication to correct the problem.

Chinese medicine, by contrast, is based on the discovery that "points" on the body surface are related to specific internal organs and their functions. By studying different disease states, the Chinese developed a model of the relationships between these surface points, the internal organs and the musculoskeletal system. Stimulating the points can change the functioning of the organs in humans and in animals.

Both acupuncture and acupressure make use of these points. Both bring about changes in body energy, the Chinese believe. But while acupuncture involves inserting needles into the body, acupressure does not. Because it is easy to learn and safe to practice, acupressure was used by common people in Japan, China and Korea.

Every human and animal is born with a fixed amount of life energy or "Chi," the Chinese believe. Chi flows through the body in pathways known as meridians. The body's meridian system can be looked at as a radio network. The acupressure points are transmitters; the organs act as receivers. The invisible meridian pathways carry messages from the acupressure points to specific parts of the body. Stimulating a point initiates a message.

Chi is used in the course of living. The organism replenishes Chi through food, water, exercise and air. Adding Chi through these sources assures that enough circulates through the body to support healthy functioning. Disease results from an external or internal imbalance in this energy. By stimulating certain points sometimes located far from the site of the symptoms, you can balance vital Chi energy and assist in the healing process.

What Can You Accomplish

Balancing Chi energy occurs in a variety of ways, governed by the body's needs. Stimulating points can release endorphins, the body's pain reducing substances. Acupressure can also relieve muscle spasms. a primary cause of pain in arthritic conditions. Point stimulation can increase the blood supply to the ailing area, increasing the supply of nutrition and oxygen to the cells. Acupressure can release the body's natural cortisone which reduces swelling. Stimulating certain points will measurably increase antibody production. The increase in immune system activity can reduce infection and relieve low grade fever. Digestion, blood flow, nervous system functions, hormone levels and the function of the organs--acupressure can affect all of these.

Chronic as well as acute equine problems respond to acupressure. Generally, a chronic problem will require three or four times as many treatments as an acute problem. The horse experiencing a particular soreness over time compensates by misusing another part of its body. Both the primary location and the compensating area require treat-ment. If treatment begins early in the development of the problem, the horse does not have an opportunity to build blockage or injure other parts of its body through compensation.

While horse owners generally consider acupressure as therapy for physical problems, it also affects attitude problems. We have seen several "bad actors" improve after only two treatments. Even ungroom-able, untouchable horses became quiet and gentle. One such was a pushy, ill-mannered Anglo-Trakehner filly. After three treatments, we returned her to her trainer to continue basic ground schooling. The trainer commented that the filly had developed a more workable attitude than before and greater willingness to learn. Another case was a 9-year-old Thoroughbred gelding who kicked and shifted whenever his owner placed him in cross-ties. After two acupressure treatments he was so much better behaved other people who kept horses at the same barn asked his owner if she'd gotten a new horse.

A Way To Prevent Problems

Ideally, you will want to apply acupressure to prevent problems. If you give your horse a twenty minute acupressure treatment two to three times weekly, you can noticeably enhance your horse's well-being. Such preventive treatments will allow you to speed up your horse's training schedule.

The ancient Oriental medical practice of acupressure gives you the opportunity to improve your horse's overall well-being and performance. The following chapters detail the acupressure process we have developed for horses and shows you how to perform this treatment on your own horse.

3. MERIDIANS

The Chinese medical term "meridian" was introduced to the English language via the French translation of the Chinese words "jingluo." "Jing" means "to go through," "luo" means "something that connects," or "a net." The pathways that carry Chi (the life force) throughout the body are the meridians. These unseen pathways are said, by Chinese meridian theory, to embody a physical reality and the Chi and blood move along them transporting nourishment, strength and healing properties. The meridian system connects and unifies the parts of the body. The Chinese believe it is imperative to maintain the meridians in a balanced state, allowing self-healing to occur.

The meridians connect the interior and exterior of the body. Stimulating acupressure points on the surface of the body therefore, affects what goes on inside of the body. Acupressure points are located along the meridians which serve as pathways for the Chi energy flowing throughout the body. Fourteen meridians exist in the bodies of all animals, including humans. Twelve meridians have a corresponding sister meridian. Sister meridians have a unique connection with each other as they are the entry and exit points for the flow of Chi energy, one is Yin and one is Yang. One meridian of the pair flows on the top side of the body and one on the underside of the body. Also, if one sister meridians has an excess of energy, the other will show a deficiency of energy. The two meridians that lack sister counterparts are the Conception Vessel Meridian (Yin) and the Governing Vessel Meridian (Yang). These two meridians have no direct connection to any of the organs.

Chi energy circulates through the meridian system once every 24 hours. The Chi energy is concentrated for approximately two hours in each of the twelve major meridians. During these periods of energy concentration, stimulation of associated meridian points will generally produce a more impactful result. A flow chart of Chi energy is shown on page 11.

Chi energy is comprised of balanced positive and negative forces, or Yin and Yang. The idea of Yin and Yang expresses the concept of balance in the Chinese medical model. Yin means the shady side of a hill. It is associated with the qualities of cold, passivity, darkness and femininity. In contrast, Yang means the sunny side of the hill. It is associated with the attributes of heat, movement, excitement, light and masculinity. All objects in the universe contain Yin and Yang. The interaction of these two opposite forces creates Chi, the life energy. The holistic approach to health stresses a balance of Yin and Yang energy between the sister meridians. These meridians are:

Yin (Solid Organs)	Yang (Hollow Organs)
Liver	Gall Bladder
Heart	Small Intestine
Spleen	Stomach
Lung	Large Intestine
Kidney	Bladder
Heart Constrictor	Triple Heater (Body Pump)

In a healthy body, a delicate balance exists between the negative and positive influences of Yin and Yang. Acupressure prevents disease by maintaining this balance and by restoring the body to a balanced state after disease or trauma has occurred. Thus re-balancing, through the stimulation of acupressure points located along the meridians, allows healing to take place within the body.

DIRECTIONAL AND TIME FLOW
OF CHI ENERGY ALONG THE MERIDIANS

Yin Meridians   **Yang Meridians**

Lung Meridian ━━━━━━━━ Large Intestine Meridian
3 - 5 AM   5 - 7 AM

Spleen Meridian ━━━━━━━ Stomach Meridian
9 - 11 AM   7 - 9 AM

Heart Meridian ━━━━━━━━ Small Intestine Meridian
11 - 1 PM   1 - 3 PM

Kidney Meridian ━━━━━━━ Bladder Meridian
5 - 7 PM   3 - 5 PM

Heart Constrictor Meridian ━━ Triple Heater Meridian
7 - 9 PM   9 - 11 PM

Liver Meridian ━━━━━━━━ Gall Bladder Meridian
1 - 3 AM   11 - 1 AM

The major functions of each meridian are:

Liver Meridian: Has three major functions. First, the liver adjusts and makes smooth the movement and flow of Chi energy throughout the body. The liver regulates the secretion of bile, and third, it rules the proper movement of all tendons, ligaments and even some of the body's muscles. Additionally, the liver stores energy and nutrients for physical activities, maintains physical energy through blood detoxification and builds resistance against disease.

Gall Bladder Meridian: The gall bladder stores and secretes bile. It balances body energy by regulating the internal hormones and secretions, and it distributes nutrients throughout the body. The gall bladder rules decisions. Excessive gall bladder Chi may be shown as anger, whereas timidity or shyness are a result of insufficient gall bladder Chi.

Heart Meridian: The heart adapts external stimuli to the internal environment of the body. The heart meridian regulates and circulates blood throughout the body.

Small Intestine Meridian: The small intestine governs the total body through the digestion and displacement of food.

Spleen Meridian: The spleen meridian governs the blood. It helps to create blood and assists in maintaining the flow of blood in its proper pathways. The spleen is also said to govern the muscles, flesh and the four limbs, as it originates and carries the Chi to these areas. The movement of the limbs, flesh and muscles is dependent upon a well balanced spleen meridian. This meridian also governs the digestion and fermentation process of the body.

Stomach Meridian: The stomach meridian relates to the functioning of the stomach and esophagus. It also assists with the reproductive and appetite mechanisms of the body.

Lung Meridian: The lung meridian takes in Chi energy from the air and builds resistance to external intrusions. It regulates the secretion of sweat and skin moistening. This meridian eliminates noxious gases through exhalation.

Large Intestine Meridian: The large intestine meridian eliminates stagnation of Chi energy through excretion. It also assists the lung meridian in its functions.

Kidney Meridian: The kidney meridian detoxifies the body's blood. It controls the internal secretion of hormones which energize the body. The kidney meridian produces bone marrow, influencing the development and repair of the bones.

Bladder Meridian: The bladder meridian connects to the part of the autonomic nervous system related to reproductive and urinary organs. It purifies the body by means of the elimination of urine.

Heart Constrictor Meridian: The heart constrictor meridian controls total nutrition and supplements the heart meridian in blood circulation.

Triple Heater Meridian: The triple heater meridian circulates energy through the entire body. It enhances the function of the lymphatic system and supplements the functions of the small intestine.

Governing Vessel Meridian: This meridian is the confluence of all yang meridians.

Conception Vessel Meridian: This meridian controls the contraction of the smooth muscles. It is the main source of inherited energy.

The bladder meridian is the longest meridian and it carries the most Chi energy. It contains points which correspond to the other meridians. These corresponding points are called associate points. Reactions caused by stimulation of associate points indicate energy imbalances within that corresponding meridian.

Following are eight meridian charts. The first six show the paired sister meridians, the next chart shows the non-paired governing and conception vessel meridians and the final chart shows all fourteen of the equine meridians.

GALL BLADDER & LIVER MERIDIANS

SOLID LINES SHOW YIN MERIDIAN; DOTTED LINES SHOW YANG MERIDIAN

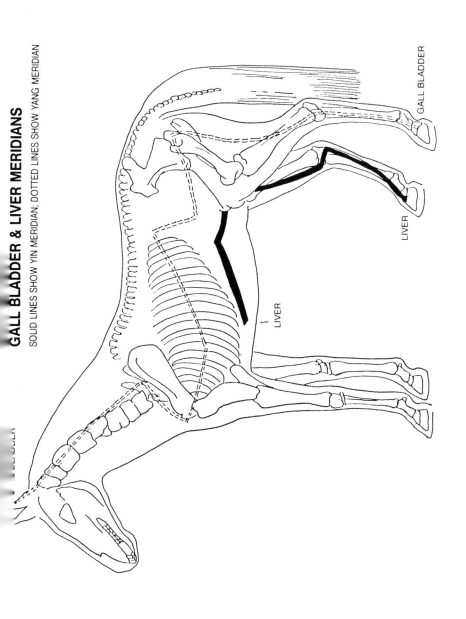

GALL BLADDER

LIVER

LIVER

15

SMALL INTESTINE & HEART MERIDIANS

SOLID LINES SHOW YIN MERIDIAN; DOTTED LINES SHOW YANG MERIDIAN

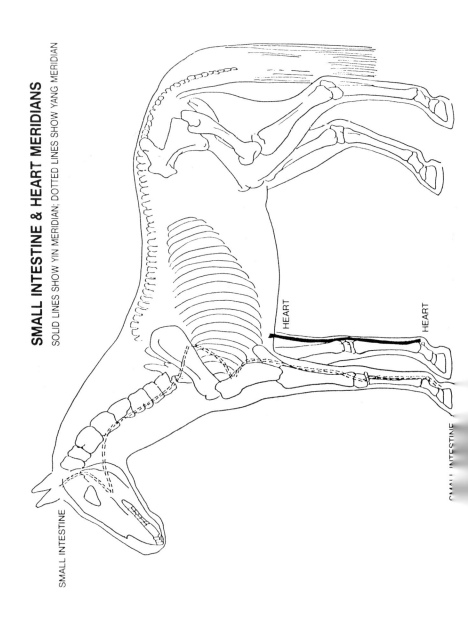

HEART

HEART

SMALL INTESTINE

SMALL INTESTINE

STOMACH & SPLEEN MERIDIANS

SOLID LINES SHOW YIN MERIDIAN; DOTTED LINES SHOW YANG MERIDIAN

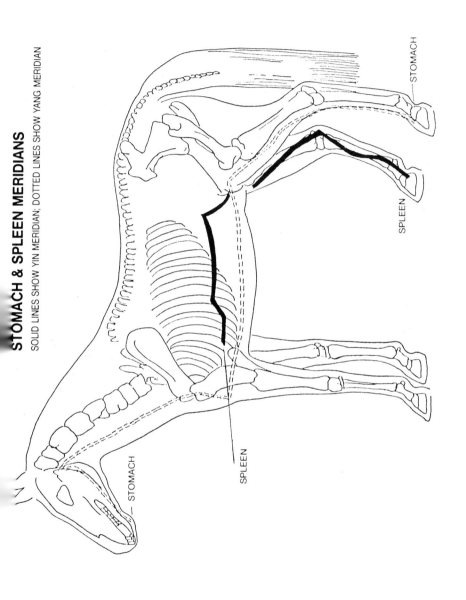

STOMACH

SPLEEN

SPLEEN

STOMACH

LARGE INTESTINE & LUNG MERIDIANS

SOLID LINES SHOW YIN MERIDIAN; DOTTED LINES SHOW YANG MERIDIAN

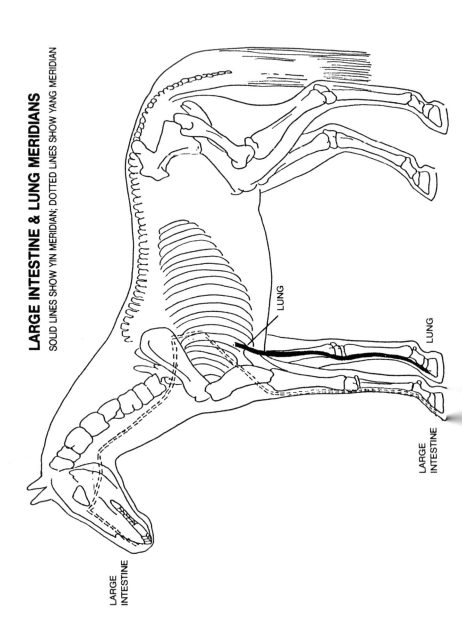

LUNG

LUNG

LARGE
INTESTINE

LARGE
INTESTINE

BLADDER & KIDNEY MERIDIANS
SOLID LINES SHOW YIN MERIDIAN; DOTTED LINES SHOW YANG MERIDIAN

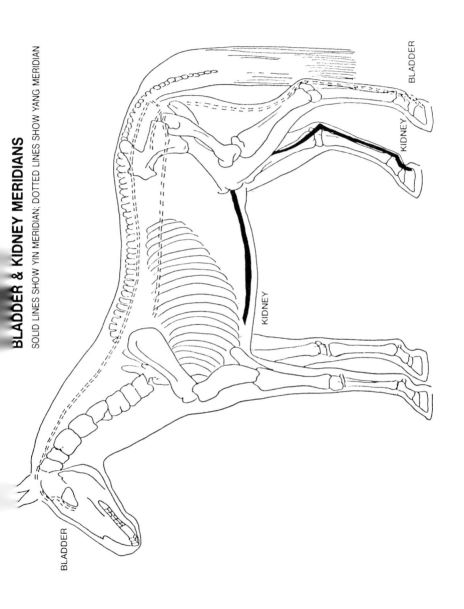

BLADDER

BLADDER

KIDNEY

KIDNEY

19

TRIPLE HEATER & HEART CONSTRICTOR MERIDIANS

SOLID LINES SHOW YIN MERIDIAN; DOTTED LINES SHOW YANG MERIDIAN

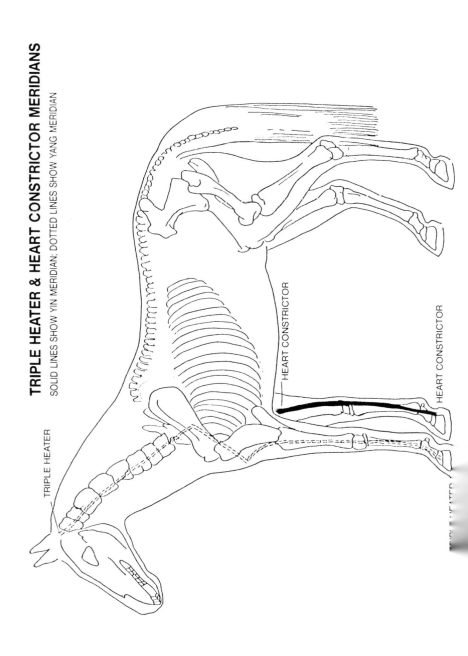

TRIPLE HEATER

HEART CONSTRICTOR

HEART CONSTRICTOR

GOVERNING VESSEL & CONCEPTION VESSEL MERIDIANS

SOLID LINES SHOW YIN MERIDIAN; DOTTED LINES SHOW YANG MERIDIAN

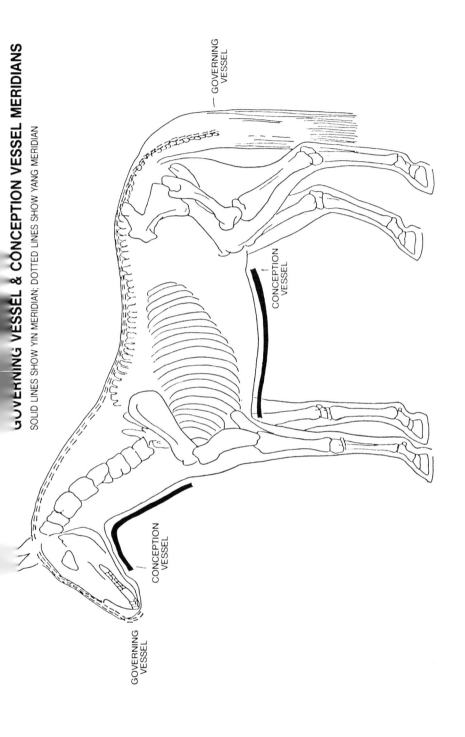

GOVERNING VESSEL

CONCEPTION VESSEL

CONCEPTION VESSEL

GOVERNING VESSEL

EQUINE MERIDIAN SYSTEM

SOLID LINES SHOW YIN MERIDIAN; DOTTED LINES SHOW YANG MERIDIAN

4. ACUPRESSURE POINTS

Acupressure points, the gateways to the 14 meridians, are located along each meridian and at other specific points on the body. Chi energy flows close to the surface of the body at the acupressure points, allowing you to manipulate that energy efficiently by using acupressure techniques to stimulate the points. In total, there are over 350 meridian points and over 250 non-meridian points.

In horses, as in humans, the therapeutic value of a point has to do with the meridian on which it is located. Stimulating points on the stomach meridian will benefit the stomach. Points on the same meridian have common values and distinct properties and effects. You can stimulate points located on the head, face and trunk to treat disorders in those areas. You can use points below the elbow and knees to treat disorders in other parts of the body.

Acupressure points are either permanent--existing at all times--or interim--appearing only during a pathological or disease state. Permanent points include:

- **Alarm Points**   Located on the surface of the abdomen. Although not found on the meridian associated with a distressed organ, they are tender when their associated organ is diseased.

- **Terminal Points**   Found at the beginning and end of a meridian, these serve as entry and exit points for Chi energy.

- **Tonification Points**   Located along a meridian line. Usually, these are cool to the touch. If you stimulate one of these points, you increase the energy flow to it and begin energy balancing.

- **Sedation Points**   Located along a meridian line, these are generally warm to the touch and slightly protruding. Stimulating these points disperses blocked energy and begins energy rebalancing.

- **Source Points**   Located in the tarsal areas, these points are important in treating internal organ diseases. Stimulating these points boosts the effects of tonification or sedation points.

- **Connecting Points** The communication point of paired meridians. Stimulating these points equalizes the Chi energy of Yin-Yang paired meridians.

- **Associated Points** Relate to the internal organs. The stimulation of these points causes tenderness if the corresponding organ is diseased.

Pressure points do not have a particular physical shape. When trying to locate a point, you should feel for its energy. The chart on the following page shows the location of the major acupressure points in the horse's body.

EQUINE ACUPRESSURE POINTS

— Carla Stroh —

5. CASE STUDIES

We would like to introduce you to some of the horses treated by Equine Acupressure, Inc. Rex, Taylor, Shanti, Rocky and the others vary in age, breed and function but they represent physical problems that performance horses are all too likely to develop during their careers.

In almost every case acupressure massage did make the horse more comfortable and mobile, although we could not restore every horse to 100 percent functioning.

Acupressure massage does not replace but complements more familiar kinds of equine medicine. The horses that came to us came at the recommendation of veterinarians, frequently after owners and vets had reached the limits of conventional treatment without achieving satisfactory results. From this perspective, we are especially proud of what acupressure massage can accomplish.

Acupressure massage can play a role in preventing injury, just as it does in bringing about recovery. A supple horse is better able to handle the demands made on him than is a tense animal. A relaxed horse will enjoy the tasks set for him more than the animal that is under a strain. For this reason, many people choose to make acupressure massage a part of their horse's everyday routine.

As effective as acupressure massage may be, the horses respond best if their owner, rider or other familiar caregiver is part of the treatment process. With this method of treatment you have an active role in healing your horse and keeping him healthy.

CASE STUDY - HIND LEG LAMENESS
Carey & Jessie

Carey took Jessie a 14-year-old Thoroughbred gelding to the veterinarian for a variety of complaints. The vet found the horse to be suffering from tendonitis, as well as from pain over his loins, rump and stifles.

After successful conventional treatment for the tendonitis, we began to treat Jessie for his hindleg and lower back problems. On close examination, Jessie showed an overall lack of muscle development in his loins and gluteal areas. He was lame in the left hind leg and short-strided with both hind legs. When trotting or cantering in a circle, Jessie tended to swing his outside leg sideways from the hip, toeing out as he did so. He held his head and neck stiffly out in front of him and showed very little shoulder extension.

During our first acupressure session, we found that not only was Jessie lame in his left hind leg but he was hypersensitive on his right side. At the same time, his left side was tense and guarded. The gelding also lacked muscle tone in his shoulders.

Several days later, after Carey had given acupressure treatments to Jessie as instructed, we once again examined the horse. He showed no lameness and was less guarded about his left side. While he could canter to the right normally, Jessie rabbit-hopped when he tried to canter to the left, lifting his hind leg with the muscles of the loin.

We taught Carey a series of stretches to improve Jessie's overall flexibility. We encouraged Carey to continue the acupressure treatment and stretches.

Two weeks later Jessie moved in a relaxed manner, using his hip normally, taking longer hind leg strides and showing improved shoulder extension. His muscle mass had increased noticeably and muscle tone in his shoulders was considerably improved. Carey uses the stretches and a maintenance acupressure regimen as part of her normal warm-up routine. She reports that Jessie continues to improve in strength and flexibility in all gaits.

CASE STUDY - LOWER BACK SORENESS
Gus & Taylor

At the suggestion of the vet school at Colorado State University, Gus, the breeding manager at a local stud farm asked us to examine Taylor, a 14-year-old Quarter Horse stallion. Taylor was severly lame in his hind legs. He had not been out of his stall in several weeks because he was unable to step over the stall door runner. Taylor's owner, Ron, and Gus were very concerned about the horse. Both questioned his ability to participate in the coming breeding season.

The stallion's veterinary diagnosis pointed to vertebral arthritis, complicated by muscle spasms in the lower back and generalized atrophy of the rump muscles.

Taylor moved stiffly at all gaits, dragging his left hind foot at almost every stride. His lameness showed clearly in the shortened forward movement of his left hind leg and the exaggerated left hip-lift he used to get the leg forward.

Our acupressure treatments concentrated on the stallion's lumbar, hip, rump and thigh areas. During the first several sessions, Taylor exhibited aggressive, protective behavior, as well as tensing his muscles in a typical guarding manner. By the third acupressure treatment, he began to relax during the session. By this time, he was also sound at the walk and extended trot. His collected trot still showed lameness of the left hind leg.

After his sixth acupressure session, we started the stallion on a light exercise program in preparation for his appearance in a stallion parade. We added light longeing and treadmill work to his acupressure treatments. Over the next several weeks we adjusted his work schedule according to his level of soundness on any given day.

We began to notice the muscles of Taylor's right lumbar area seemed overdeveloped in comparison to his left side. The right lumbar area also showed an increased amount of sensitivity. As Taylor's course of treatment progressed, this sensitivity lessened but did not disappear.

Approximately three months after his initial vet examination Taylor made a successful appearance in the scheduled stallion parade. He has since completed two breeding seasons without a significant recurrence of lameness in his hind leg.

Unlike most of the horses we see, Taylor's treatment was geared to attaining results by a given date. Maintenance treatments were not administered after that date. However, 20 months after his last acupressure treatment, Taylor is sound enough to be exercised regularly and shown to prospective breeders.

This case showed us the importance of participation by the owner or caretaker of the horse. Personnel from Equine Acupressure, Inc. administered all of Taylor's treatments. Progress is slower when the horse's owner, caretaker or rider is not involved in the treatment. With that involvement, horses show significant improvement in one to six weeks, regardless of the problem the horse presented initially.

CASE STUDY - HIND LEG LAMENESS
Mark & Rex

A veterinarian examined Rex, a 10-year-old Arabian gelding, for frequent soreness of his back, lower back and hind legs. Mark, Rex's owner, called us when Rex refused to move after light riding.

When we observed Rex, we saw a distinct uneasiness at the trot in either direction and a tendency for the horse to move with his hindquarters directed toward the outside of the circle. A shortened stride or hopping movement was also apparent, primarily of the right hind leg. In addition, Rex seemed fidgety, exhibiting a variety of nervous actions.

In the first acupressure session, we concentrated on Rex's hind legs and lower back problems. We worked points along the bladder meridian, beginning at Rex's mid-neck and extending over his rump. We worked points along the stomach meridian, beginning at mid-barrel and extending down the inside of the hind legs. We also stimulated lumbar, hip and thigh points. We showed Mark the technique, teaching him which points to work and some stretches. We suggested he perform the massage every other day for 10 days.

Mark diligently followed the schedule we developed for Rex. At our second session, Rex's movements and attitude were much improved. Rex seemed generally more relaxed. He moved more evenly and without hitching at the trot. Mark was able to take him on trail rides, stopping if he noticed any soreness in the horse to work a few points. Then he and Rex were able to continue on for a pleasant ride.

By our third session, Rex moved freely and evenly at all gaits. Mark continues to use acupressure treatments as needed. Currently Rex is enjoying use as a trail/pleasure horse. Mark's four to six hour rides in the Rocky Mountain terrain present no problem for Rex.

CASE STUDY - HOLLOWED BACK
Liz & Rocky

Liz brought Rocky, a 13-year-old Tennessee Walking Horse gelding to an individual training clinic we held in Pennsylvania. Liz uses Rocky for pleasure/trail riding. She became concerned about Rocky when he developed a soreness over the length of his back from mid-barrel to rump. She tried different saddles to relieve the soreness, but noticed no appreciable difference.

When we began Rocky's acupressure treatment his back was severely hollowed, with bilateral reactive points on the bladder meridian. He also exhibited shoulder soreness, which is often a compensatory symptom.

We worked Rocky three times. With each treatment, the severity of his hollowed back decreased. By the third session his back regained normal posture. Liz rode him home and reported that his gaits were much smoother and his attitude more willing than had been true in some time.

We taught Liz the acupressure treatment we used on Rocky. She continues to keep him in shape with several sessions each week.

Marie shows Liz the acupressure treatment for Rocky's hollowed back.

31

CASE STUDY - SHOULDER SORENESS
Elaine & Nabiel

At her veterinarian's suggestion, Elaine brought Nabiel to us for treatment of longstanding lameness in both front legs. A 7-year-old Arabian gelding, Nabiel moved by shortening the stride of his right front leg and swinging the left one out. It seemed probable that Nabiel had suffered some kind of injury at some time, since his left shoulder showed generalized scarring and atrophy of the scapular muscles.

Our first session with Nabiel concentrated on the shoulder lameness. We worked points on the shoulder, forearm and neck, as well as on the lumbar, hip, rump and thigh areas. Although they were located far from the demonstrated lameness, the points in these last named areas were sensitive and reactive. As is common in horses with a longstanding soreness, Nabiel compensated for his shoulder problems by using his loin and rump muscles incorrectly. This led to the reactivity there. As we treated Nabiel he reacted with general agitation, protective behavior, guarding and muscle spasms. We taught Elaine a program of point work she should do every other day for ten days.

When we returned for a second session with Nabiel the gelding exhibited greater freedom of movement in his shoulder. His extension and flexibility were much improved. We repeated the point work of the first session, but added eight points on Nabiel's chest and forearm. We taught Elaine a series of stretches designed to increase his flexibility and range of motion.

We called a chiropractor to work with us at the third session. He adjusted Nabiel's neck and lumbosacral area. The previous acupressure massage work greatly facilitated these adjustments. We developed a maintenance regimen of massage for Elaine. She uses it as needed with the result that Nabiel is consistently rideable at this time. He shows marked improvement in both attitude and performance.

CASE STUDY - ARTHRITIS
Laura Lee & Shanti

Laura Lee brought Shanti, an 8-year-old Morgan mare, to us for acupressure treatment on referral from Colorado State University. Shanti's diagnosis was arthritis of the shoulder and elbow. Traditional veterinary treatments brought about no significant improvement in the formerly graceful driving horse.

When she came to us, Shanti was so stiff and sore that she could not trot normally. Instead she shuffled awkwardly over the ground.

We performed a series of acupressure treatments, instructing Laura Lee on the points and stretches to work. The program for Shanti concentrated on the stomach, large intestine and gall bladder meridians. Laura Lee did front leg stretches every other day. Shanti's problem was chronic and during the first three acupressure sessions, she did not exhibit obvious reactions. During the fourth session, Shanti reacted to treatment with head tossing, kicking, attempted biting and front leg pawing. We attribute these reactions to the chronic nature of her problems and the gravity of the blockages. It is unusual that it took three sessions to reach the depth of Shanti's blockages. Shanti's reactions serve as a reminder that you should position yourself safely when you work on your horse.

After six weeks of treatments Shanti showed less soreness and was again able to trot. Shanti could not return to her former use as a driving horse, but Laura Lee uses her as a pleasure mount.

6. ACUPRESSURE TREATMENT

There are four phases of acupressure treatment, each necessary for the horse to receive full benefit. These phases are opening, point work, closing and meridian stretches. In all phases of acupressure work, it is important for you to have a relaxed attitude and a listening approach to your horse. Before beginning the treatment, clear your mind of the days activity and focus on your own Chi energy. Allow your breathing to become deep and relaxed. This will assist in balancing your horses Chi energy and promote healing.

Depending on the nature of your horse's ailment and your proficiency level at giving the treatment, it can take from 25 minutes to one hour to complete the acupressure treatment. Generally the opening will take five to ten minutes, point work ten to thirty minutes, closing five to ten minutes and stretches five to twenty minutes.

When starting an acupressure treatment, choose a familiar and comfortable location for your horse. We do not recommend that you cross tie your horse. Cross ties restrict head movement which can indicate pain, relaxation or curiosity. The ideal situation is shown in the photograph below. The horse is haltered and your helper is holding the lead rope. While you work your helper can watch for the horse's reactions, particularly on the side opposite you.

Helper holds horse loosely and assists with treatment by watching for reactions.

34

Your horse can react to all phases of the acupressure treatment. If you notice and keep track of these reactions, they will provide cues to problem areas and serve as guideposts in ongoing treatments.

Reactions such as back hollowing, tail crooking, leg lifting or muscle spasms are very obvious. As reactions occur, jot them down in a notebook, specifying the phase in which they occur. For example, "First acupressure treatment produced muscle spasms of the lower back, lasting for 10-15 seconds. Spasms occured during point work. In the closing phase the muscle spasms recurred, lasting approximately five seconds." By doing this, you will have an on-going record of your horse's reactions, changes and progress.

Equally important are the less obvious signs your horse will exhibit. Subtle reactions include: facial expression changes, softening of the eye, neck twisting, tongue rolling or stretching, chewing, moving into or away from the point pressure or leg stretching. This is not an exhaustive list of reactions. You should view any behavior unusual for your horse as a reaction. Your list will increase your awareness of your horse's body and its healing process.

You may find that your horse will be tender following an acupressure treatment. Do not be alarmed. It takes 24 hours for Chi energy to cycle throughout the body, therefore it generally takes 24 to 36 hours for your horse to show improvement.

Under certain conditions, you should not give an acupressure treatment to your horse. These include:

DO NOT GIVE ACUPRESSURE TREATMENT IF:

1. Your horse is pregnant.
2. Your horse has just been fed. Wait three to four hours after the horse eats.
3. Your horse is lathered from a strenuous workout. Wait until he cools down.
4. Your horse has just bred or been bred. Wait 12 hours before treating a stallion.
5. Your horse has a high fever.
6. Your horse has an infectious disease.

OPENING

"Opening" is the first phase of an acupressure treatment. It introduces the treatment to your horse in a nonthreatening and relaxing manner. The opening allows your horse to become aware of its body in preparation for point work.

With your helper loosely holding your horse, you are ready to begin the opening. On a horse, an acupressure opening is performed from front to rear and from top to bottom, following the direction of energy flow along the meridian lines. When doing an opening, position the palm in full contact with the horse, using approximately five pounds of pressure. Glide your palm over your horse's body, shaping your hands to its contours. This technique relaxes the horse and allows you to distinguish differences in your horse's body temperature and muscle tone. It also allows you to feel for surface protrusions or depressions.

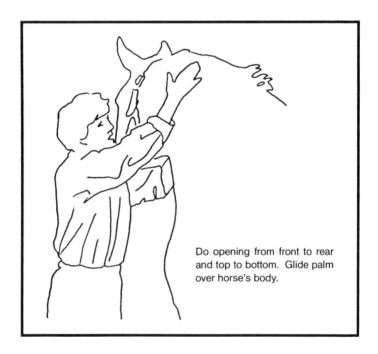

Do opening from front to rear and top to bottom. Glide palm over horse's body.

Stroke downward from the neck to the withers, and again from the withers to the croup along the bladder meridian. Then, using firm pressure, stroke from the croup, over the rump and down the rear leg to the hock. Repeat the opening procedure two to three times. If your horse is too tall for you to reach his withers to apply the proper amount of pressure, use a stool to increase your height and gain leverage.

When doing an opening, watch for signs of sensitivity, areas of heat or coolness, and any reactions from your horse. Also note the different characteristics within the various muscles, for example rigidity or mushiness or protrusions or depressions. These characteristics may indicate a meridian block and signal that point work is necessary.

REVIEW OF OPENING PROCEDURE

1. Position your horse in a comfortable and familiar location.
2. Place your palm in full contact with your horse.
3. Exert approximately five pounds of pressure.
4. Glide your palm from front to rear, top to bottom of your horse.
5. Watch for and note reactions or areas of sensitivity.
6. Repeat opening two to three times on both sides.

POINT WORK

Point work stimulates specific points along a meridian line. It is the foundation of acupressure treatment and its second phase. When you stimulate individual points along the meridian lines you release energy blockages and allow the horse to assist in its own healing process. Equine musculoskeletal ailments respond dramatically to this work.

You may choose from three methods to do point work. Use the one you find most comfortable or effective for you. These are the thumb technique, the elbow technique or the "circular thumb" technique. You may also use a combination of these techniques on your horse during an acupressure treatment.

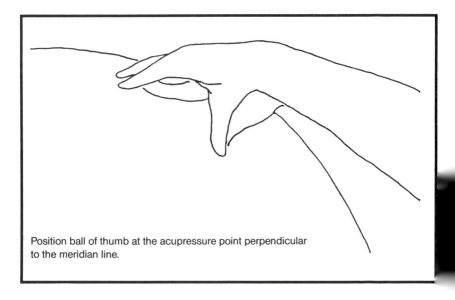

Position ball of thumb at the acupressure point perpendicular to the meridian line.

When you do point work, position the ball of your thumb at the acupressure point perpendicular to the individual meridian line along which you are working. As in the opening phase, point work is done from front to rear and top to bottom. Stimulate each point for three to five seconds. It is difficult to state specifically how much pressure should be used. The best procedure is to use gentle pressure at first, then increase it as your horse allows.

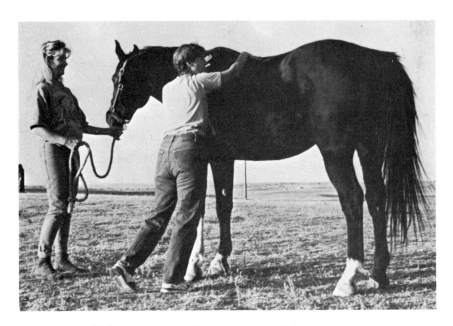

Marie showing owner the acupressure technique.
Notice that she is using her whole body to lean into a point.

Gently put pressure into a point and slowly release out of a point. Use your entire body when doing this work. When stimulating a point, straighten your arm at the elbow and lean into the point with partial body weight. Do not just use your thumbs. Performing the treatment in this manner saves your fingers and wrists from unnecessary fatigue and minimizes any tendency to "jab" at the point. Synchronize your breathing pattern with point stimulation. Breathe out while easing into the point and breathe in while releasing the point. It is common for the horse to also synchronize its breathing with you after several treatments.

Another method you can use in doing point work is the elbow technique. This technique is useful if you have weak or injured thumbs. The elbow technique affords you a great deal more leverage and pressure, therefore, it is suggested that you use it only after you have become proficient and comfortable with thumb point work.

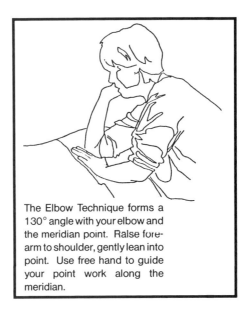

The Elbow Technique forms a 130° angle with your elbow and the meridian point. Raise forearm to shoulder, gently lean into point. Use free hand to guide your point work along the meridian.

Place your elbow in a point with your forearm at approximately a 130 degree angle. Slowly raise your forearm toward your shoulder as you gently lean your body weight into the point. Return your forearm to the original 130 degree angle, lean out of the point and repeat the technique at the next point.

The elbow technique is most often used for working points on the bladder meridian. If necessary, use a stool to gain height for proper angling.

Standing on the bucket gives Marie extra height and leverage for the Elbow Technique.

Another acupressure method you can use on your horse is the "circular thumb" technique. In this method you apply direct pressure to the point with one thumb. Gently ease into the point, applying three to five pounds of pressure. Next, while continuing to apply pressure, rotate your thumb in a circular motion. Complete three to six full revolutions. Release gently from the point and move on to the next point and repeat the technique. While using the circular thumb technique keep your free hand on your horse. The constant contact with your horse is comforting to him and helps you feel muscle spasms, twitching or other reactions to the point work.

Based on your horse's reaction to the opening, work along the meridian lines, focusing on specific areas of energy blockage. A spontaneous pain reaction at any point may indicate a disorder in that particular meridian. Tenderness, revealed by heavy pressure, indicates that the meridian is deficient in Chi energy. Tenderness, revealed by light pressure, identifies an excess of Chi energy.

In the opening phase of the treatment, you were asked to feel for depressions or protrusions on your horse. The points which protrude, called "jitsu," indicate areas of excessive energy. The depressed points, called "kyo," show a deficiency of energy.

Jitsu points are warm to the touch. If you stimulate these points, you will generally get an immediate response from the horse. He may shy away, move the limb you touch or hollow out his back.

Stimulate jitsu points gently, holding for three to five seconds in order to begin releasing the blockage. Points located away from the jitsu area also need to be stimulated to open them and draw the energy excess away from the jitsu point. This procedure begins to balance your horse's energy and is known as a sedation process. The circular thumb technique is particularly beneficial when used to sedate the jitsu or hot points you locate along a meridian. When you stimulate the hot points you will disperse Chi energy away from those points and begin to restore balance to your horse.

Kyo points, or energy deficient areas, are cooler in temperature than the surrounding area. Kyo points require longer stimulation. The best indicator of sufficient point stimulation is a warming of the kyo point. This can take anywhere from 15 seconds to one minute, or longer. When you stimulate the kyo's surrounding meridian points you draw energy and strength into the deficient area and normalize the entire body's energy flow.

With regular acupressure work, you can keep acute, or jitsu problems, from becoming chronic or more serious ailments. Generally speaking, a chronic ailment in your horse will show up as a kyo condition while an acute ailment will show up as jitsu. A kyo condition might take longer to correct because the horse's healing power is depleted. Patience and strengthening treatments are required for this condition.

REVIEW OF POINT WORK PROCEDURE

1. Place thumb perpendicular to meridian line.
2. Stimulate point by gently easing into and out of the point.
3. Work points from front to rear, top to bottom.
4. Identify cool and warm areas, stimulate warm areas for three to five seconds, stimulate cool areas for 15 seconds or longer.
5. Watch for and note reactions or areas of sensitivity.
6. Repeat point work on each side of your horse.

CLOSING

The third phase of the acupressure treatment is the closing. It has two purposes. First, closing connects the energy flow between the points stimulated during point work. This re-establishes a more balanced energy flow along the meridian lines. Secondly, the closing work begins re-patterning cellular memory. Cellular memory has been described by kinesiologists as a learned response at the individual cellular level to a chronic stimulus such as pain. The acupressure closing phase replaces the cell's previously learned negative response with a positive phenomenon.

You may choose from three types of closings. Whichever one you choose for your horse, do it twice on each side of your horse to complete the closing.

The first closing technique is the same as the opening phase discussed earlier. It is known as the "smooth hand" technique. Position the palm of your hand in full contact with the horse, using approximately five pounds of pressure. Glide your palm over the horse's body from front to rear, and top to bottom.

The second technique is known as "cupped hand" percussion. Position your hand in a relaxed "pyramid" shape. A side view looks like an "A." When you execute this technique your palm should not make contact with the horse. Remember, keep your wrists relaxed. Use your two hands to alternately strike the body of your horse in a continuously rhythmic motion. If your hands make a bass sound as you strike, you have positioned your hands properly and are keeping your wrists loose. As in the opening, begin the closing at the neck of your horse, moving from front to rear and top to bottom. This closing results in a stimulating yet relaxing finish.

Both the first and second closing techniques are illustrated on the following page.

"Smooth Hand" Closing

"Cupped Hand" Closing

The illustration below shows the third type of closing. Use both hands in a light rocking motion. Apply pressure through the palms. Move two to three inches down the horse's body with each rocking movement. Again, the direction of work is from front to rear, and top to bottom. Repeat the closing you choose twice.

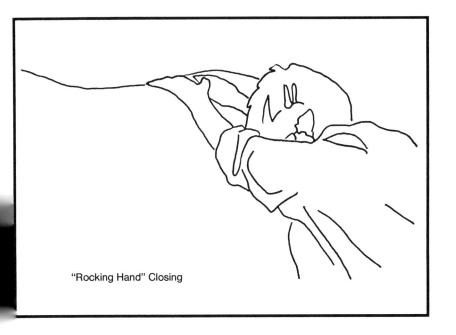

"Rocking Hand" Closing

REVIEW OF CLOSING PROCEDURE

1. Choose any one of the three optional closing techniques.
2. Close your horse from front to rear, top to bottom.
3. Repeat closing two to three times on both sides of your horse.

REVIEW OF ACUPRESSURE TREATMENT

OPENING

1. Position your horse in a comfortable and familiar location.
2. Place your palm in full contact with your horse.
3. Exert approximately five pounds of pressure.
4. Glide your palm from front to rear, top to bottom of your horse.
5. Watch for and note reactions or areas of sensitivity.
6. Repeat opening two to three times on both sides.

POINT WORK

1. Place thumb perpendicular to meridian line.
2. Stimulate point by gently easing into and out of the point.
3. Work points from front to rear, top to bottom.
4. Identify cool and warm areas, stimulate warm areas for three to five seconds, stimulate cool areas for 15 seconds or longer.
5. Watch for and note reactions or areas of sensitivity.
6. Repeat point work on each side of your horse.

CLOSING

1. Choose any one of the three optional closing techniques.
2. Close your horse from front to rear, top to bottom.
3. Repeat closing two to three times on both sides of your horse.

DO NOT GIVE ACUPRESSURE TREATMENT IF:

1. Your horse is pregnant.

2. Your horse has just been fed. Wait three to four hours after the horse eats.

3. Your horse is lathered from a strenuous workout. Wait until he cools down.

4. Your horse has just bred or been bred. Wait 12 hours before treating a stallion.

5. Your horse has a high fever.

6. Your horse has an infectious disease.

7. ACUPRESSURE STRETCHES

The stretches make up the fourth phase of acupressure treatment. These exercises are designed to improve the overall flexibility of your horse and to improve performance regardless of the activity you and your horse are involved in. The stretches complement the use of acupressure treatment. These stretches help open certain meridian lines on which the individual acupressure points are located.

To ensure maximum benefit and to avoid problems, make all stretching movements slow and fluid. As you do the exercise, hold the leg in full extension or flexion with consistent traction, --no bouncing. Always replace your horse's leg to its original position. Do not allow your horse to pull its leg away.

The stretches complement earlier acupressure treatment and serve four purposes. First, they open the meridians, enhancing the energy flow. Second, they relax and tone muscles, improving suppleness. Third, they increase flexibility which improves performance and prevents injury. Fourth, they aid in rehabilitative therapy.

Use your entire body to lift your horse's leg when you do these exercises, not just your back muscles. For safety, consider your horse's probable reaction to the stretches. In all instances, advance slowly and with caution.

FRONT LEG STRETCHES

1. Triceps Muscle Stretch

Stand facing your horse. Grasp the foreleg above the knee with both hands. Bring the knee directly upward, about waist high or to the point where resistance is felt. Hold the leg at the highest point for a count of five, then slowly replace leg to original position. Repeat exercise once.

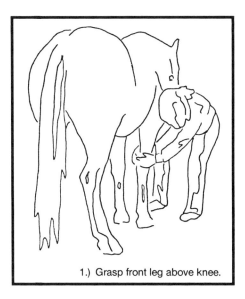

1.) Grasp front leg above knee.

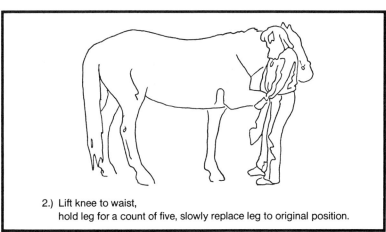

2.) Lift knee to waist,
hold leg for a count of five, slowly replace leg to original position.

2. Shoulder Extension Stretch

Stand facing your horse. Grasp the foreleg above the knee and lift until the toe is about four inches off the ground. Slowly pull the horse's knee toward your knee, asking your horse for a full shoulder extension. Gently place your horse's toe as far in front as it will permit. If your horse holds its leg where you place it, you will know that the stretch was within its capability. If your horse moves its leg backward, it is shifting to a position of comfort, telling you that the stretch was outside its capability. Ask the horse to hold the extension for a count of five. Repeat exercise once.

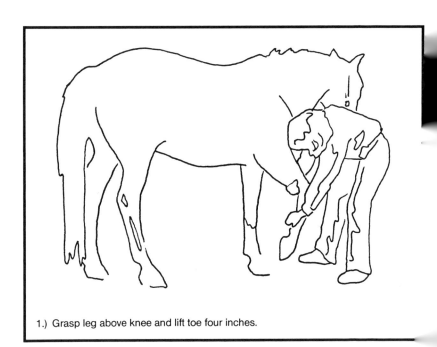

1.) Grasp leg above knee and lift toe four inches.

2.) Pull knee towards you, ask for full extension.

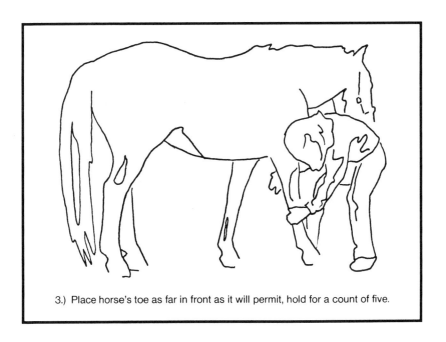

3.) Place horse's toe as far in front as it will permit, hold for a count of five.

51

3. Shoulder Flexion Stretch

Stand beside your horse's barrel facing forward. Grasp your horse's leg just above the knee with your inside hand, using your outside hand to support the fetlock joint. Using gentle traction with your inside hand, move your horse's front leg directly back toward its hind leg. Stop when resistance is felt. Hold the leg for a count of five. Return the leg to its original position and repeat exercise once.

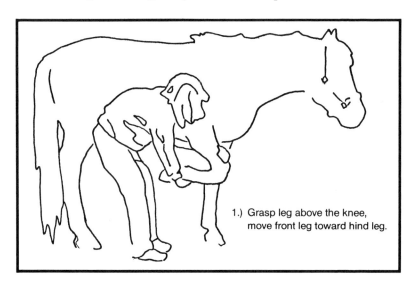

1.) Grasp leg above the knee, move front leg toward hind leg.

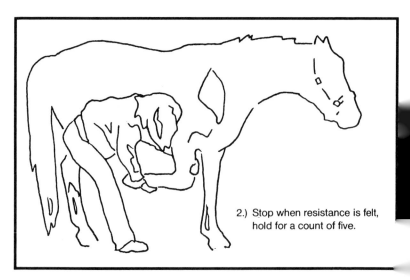

2.) Stop when resistance is felt, hold for a count of five.

4. Heel Stretch

Stand at your horse's shoulder, facing forward. Grasp the front leg as shown below. Direct the toe backward and downward. Place the toe down first, then the heel. Your horse's shoulder should be extended backwards. Ask your horse to hold the position for a count of five. Again, if your horse refuses to hold the position, the stretch is beyond its capabilities. Repeat exercise once.

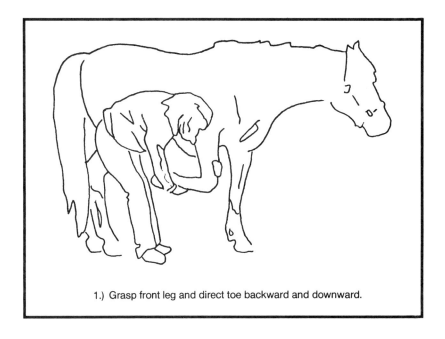

1.) Grasp front leg and direct toe backward and downward.

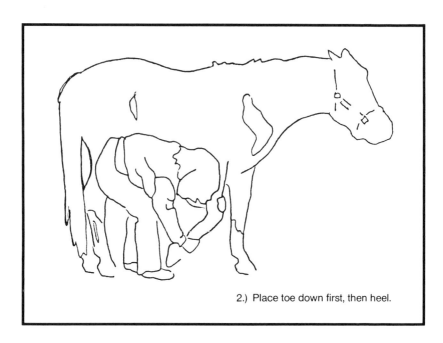

2.) Place toe down first, then heel.

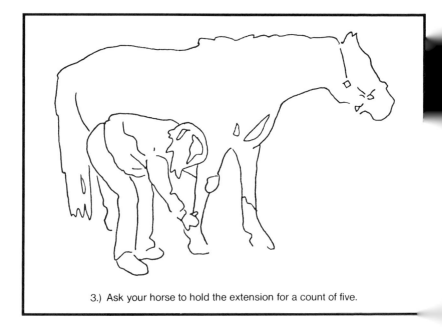

3.) Ask your horse to hold the extension for a count of five.

REAR LEG STRETCHES

1. Buttocks Stretch

Standing at the flank, face toward the rear of your horse. With your inside hand, grasp your horse's gaskin from the inside of the leg. Support the lower leg with your outside hand on the canon bone. Using gentle traction with your inside hand, pull the hind leg directly forward, (as it would go if the horse were taking a step). Stop when you feel resistance. Hold for a count of five. Replace the leg to its original position. Repeat exercise once.

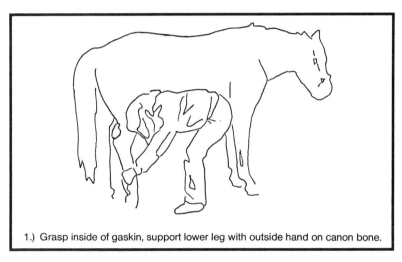

1.) Grasp inside of gaskin, support lower leg with outside hand on canon bone.

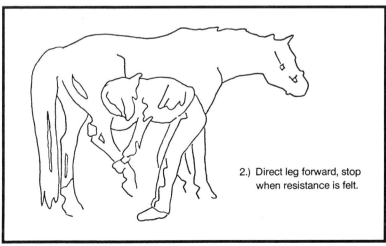

2.) Direct leg forward, stop when resistance is felt.

2. Hip Flexion/Stifle Extension Stretch

Facing the rear of your horse, grasp the hind leg and lift so that the toe is about four inches off the ground. Direct the toe forward and onto the ground in the position of a normal hind leg stride. If your horse holds its leg where you place it, you will know that the stretch is within its capability. If your horse moves its leg backward, it is shifting to a position of comfort, telling you that the stretch was outside its capability. Repeat exercise once.

1.) Grasp hind leg & lift toe about four inches off the ground.

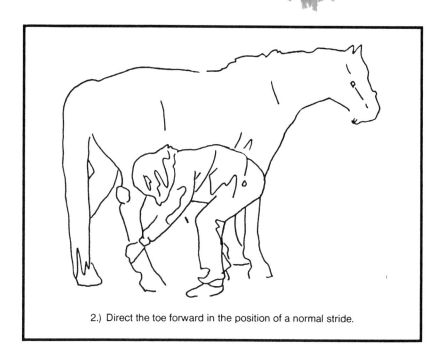

2.) Direct the toe forward in the position of a normal stride.

3.) Hold leg at normal stride extension for a count of five.

CIRCULAR FLEXIBILITY STRETCHES

The next exercises will improve the flexibility of your horse's shoulder, elbow and hip regions. The dance stretch makes for suppleness and better coordination of the rear legs. This exercise is valuable for dressage horses and for horses doing other performance activities. For best results, strive for fluidity of movement as you did in the previous exercises.

1. Rear Leg Dance Stretch

Stand at your horse's back leg, facing its rear. Grasp the hind leg with hands at either end of the canon bone. Direct the leg forward, and touch the toe to the ground. Then direct the leg to the side, and touch the toe to the ground. Finally, direct the leg to the rear, and touch the toe to the ground. Hold the leg at each point in the semi-circle for a count of two. Replace the leg to its original position. Repeat exercise once.

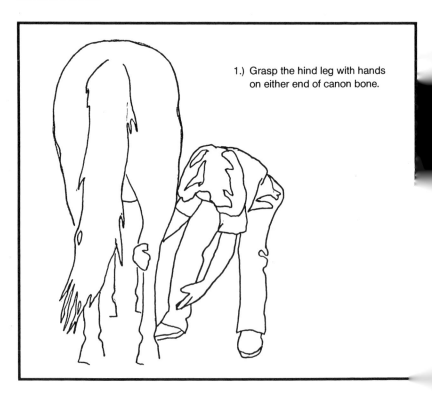

1.) Grasp the hind leg with hands on either end of canon bone.

2.) Direct leg forward and touch toe to the ground.

3.) Direct leg to side and touch toe to the ground.

4.) Direct leg to the rear and touch toe to the ground.

2. Shoulder Rotation Stretch

Stand in front of your horse, facing its forelegs. Grasp the front leg above the knee with both hands. Raise the knee to the point of resistance and then lower the knee approximately one inch. Slowly rotate the foreleg in complete circles. Start with small circles and gradually increase the diameter. Reverse the direction of rotation. Rotate the foreleg five times in each direction.

1.) Grasp front leg above knee, with both hands raise knee to point of resistance, then lower one inch.

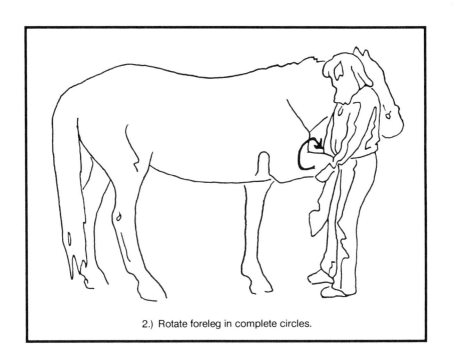

2.) Rotate foreleg in complete circles.

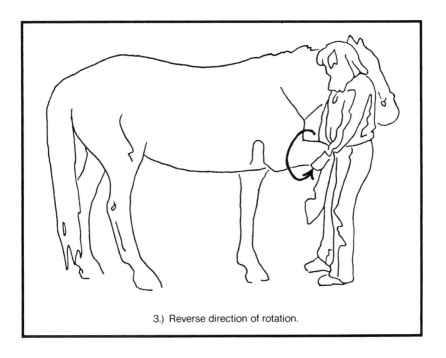

3.) Reverse direction of rotation.

NECK STRETCHES

This exercise improves your horse's neck flexibility. The stretches serve to open meridians, specifically the bladder and small intestine, aiding the acupressure treatment.

1.) Brace forearm against neck about six inches from poll, direct horse's head toward you on a level plane.

Stand at your horse's head facing forward. Grasp the halter as illustrated above. Place your free arm on the horse's neck approximately six inches from its poll. Slowly move your horse's head towards you, while bracing your forearm against its neck. Pull the head steadily toward you until you feel resistance. When turning the horse's head toward you keep it level. Do not pull just the nose toward your body.

For the second stretch move your forearm down the horse's neck approximately 12 inches from its poll and repeat the exercise as shown below.

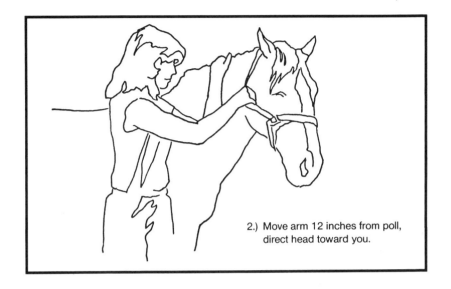

2.) Move arm 12 inches from poll, direct head toward you.

For the third stretch, move your forearm approximately 20 inches from the horse's poll and repeat the exercise. Repeat the three stretches two times in each direction.

3.) Move arm 20 inches from poll, direct head toward you.

BACK STRETCHES

These exercises build strength in your horse's abdominal muscles and increase back flexibility. Strengthening these muscles allows your horse to use them properly and bend more fully. The horse will be able to maintain a better topline and collect itself more fully.

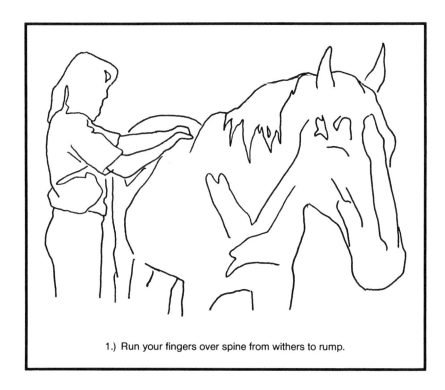

1.) Run your fingers over spine from withers to rump.

Stand at the side of your horse and run your fingers over its spine from the withers to the rump. Use strong pressure to make your horse hollow out its back. In the same position, run your fingers along the center of your horse's abdomen from its forelegs to its navel, wriggling your fingers as you press upward. Use strong pressure to make your horse flex its back. Repeat exercise three times.

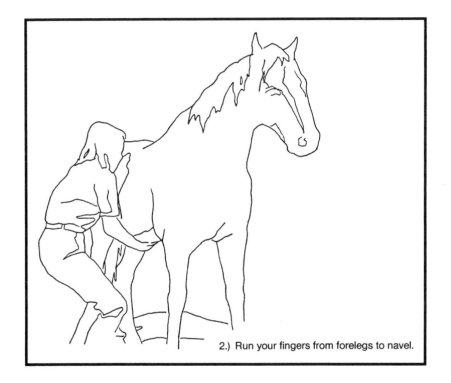

2.) Run your fingers from forelegs to navel.

8. ACUPRESSURE MAINTENANCE TREATMENT

Just as acupressure treatments are invaluable for the ailing horse, they can help horses that are not sick or injured maintain their well-being. Two to four acupressure treatments per week, will keep your horse's energy meridians open and balanced. This balanced state of energy flow will improve your horse's overall attitude and will keep minor aches from turning into a major ailment. By doing the acupressure stretches two to four times per week, you will increase your horse's suppleness and decrease the possibility of muscle strains.

Many horse owners simply make the acupressure treatment part of their established warming up or cooling down routines. Try each with your horse and choose what works best for you.

To do the maintenance treatment, open your horse as described in Chapter 6. Remember to work on your horse in a place familiar to him and where he feels comfortable. Remember also to clear your mind of the days activities and focus on yourself and your horse. Do the opening from front to back, and top to bottom. This phase should take between three to eight minutes.

MAINTENANCE TREATMENT

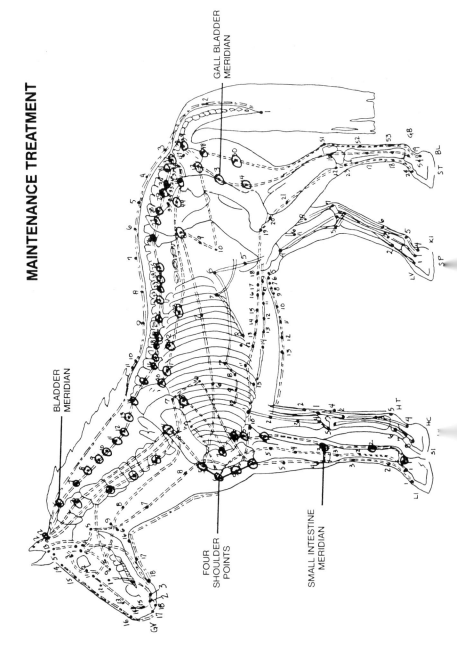

GALL BLADDER MERIDIAN

BLADDER MERIDIAN

FOUR SHOULDER POINTS

SMALL INTESTINE MERIDIAN

MAINTENANCE TREATMENT

Point Work

1. Stimulate the bladder meridian from the head over to the croup.
2. Stimulate the small intestine meridian from the neck to the bottom of the foreleg.
3. Work the gall bladder points as shown.
4. Work the four points on the chest of your horse as shown.
5. Watch for and note reactions and areas of sensitivity.
6. Close your horse, working from front to rear, top to bottom.

Stretches

1. Do triceps muscle stretch.
2. Do shoulder extension stretch.
3. Do shoulder flexion stretch.
4. Do heel stretch.
5. Do buttocks stretch.
6. Do hip flexion/stifle extension stretch.
7. Do shoulder rotation stretch.
8. Do neck and back stretches.

Frequency

Do the maintenance acupressure treatment two to four times per week.

9. ACUPRESSURE TREATMENT FOR SPECIFIC PROBLEMS

The following pages describe treatments we at Equine Acupressure, Inc., developed and used to heal such frequently seen problems as lower back soreness, neck stiffness and founder. Four years of study and casework with performance horses formed the basis for the procedures we recommend. We adapted and modified the ancient Chinese medical practices underlying acupressure massage to arrive at these treatments.

Where the owner has been consistent with the treatment, each horse presented to us has shown significant improvement.

When you do the treatments, do the acupressure work as a unit. Begin with the opening, complete the point work, close your horse, and then do the suggested stretches. Again, we recommend that you consult your veterinarian for all equine ailments. Acupressure work is not a substitute for traditional veterinary medicine, but a complement to it.

NECK STIFFNESS

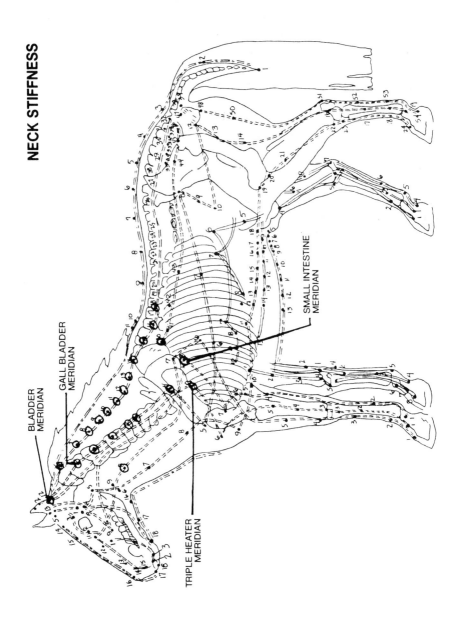

BLADDER MERIDIAN

GALL BLADDER MERIDIAN

TRIPLE HEATER MERIDIAN

SMALL INTESTINE MERIDIAN

NECK STIFFNESS

Shows Up As:
- Resistance to lateral bending
- Inappropriate flexing at the poll
- Head tossing
- Inappropriate head carriage

Refer to drawing on opposite page for points to be worked.

Procedure

To relieve your horse's neck stiffness, stimulate the points shown in the drawing, working from front to back. After opening your horse, stimulate the bladder meridian by applying pressure to each point for three to five seconds. Repeat point work two times. Stimulate the noted points on the small intestine, gall bladder and triple heater meridians in the same manner. Hold points which produce a reaction for ten to fifteen seconds, or longer. Typical reactions include, head tossing, avoidance, laying ears back, nose extending, excessive mouth and lip movement and muscle spasms. Close your horse as previously described.

Stretches

Perform the neck stretches, shoulder rotation and shoulder extension stretches. Do the acupressure treatment on one day and the stretches on the alternate day.

requency

Administer acupressure treatment and stretches every other day for one week.

SHOULDER SORENESS

GALL BLADDER MERIDIAN

LARGE INTESTINE MERIDIAN

STOMACH MERIDIAN

TRIPLE HEATER MERIDIAN

SMALL INTESTINE MERIDIAN

SHOULDER SORENESS

Shows Up As:
- Restricted front leg mobility
- Off beat cadence
- Shuffling gait
- Lameness

Refer to drawing on opposite page for points to be worked.

Procedure

Stimulation of the noted points will relieve shoulder soreness. First work the points along the small intestine meridian, holding each for three to five seconds. Next, stimulate the points shown on the large intestine meridian. Finally, stimulate the points shown on the triple heater, stomach, and gall bladder meridians. Stimulate the meridian points from front to rear, top to bottom, doing each meridian line two times on both sides of your horse. Reactions to look for include, front leg extension, neck twisting, muscle spasms, and avoidance. Hold reactive points for ten to fifteen seconds.

Stretches

Do the triceps muscle, shoulder extension, shoulder flexion and shoulder rotation stretches.

Frequency

Administer the acupressure treatment and stretches every other day for one week, or until the condition subsides. Do the acupressure treatment on one day and the stretches on the alternate day.

STIFLE LAMENESS

BLADDER MERIDIAN

GALL BLADDER MERIDIAN

STOMACH MERIDIAN

LIVER MERIDIAN

SPLEEN MERIDIAN

STIFLE LAMENESS

Shows Up As: • Lack of rear leg propulsion
  • Lameness
  • Subtle to moderate uneven rear leg ـ
  • Crossing over or tracking wide

Refer to drawing on opposite page for points to be worked.

Procedure

Stifle lameness can be rectified by working the liver, bladder, spleen, gall bladder and stomach meridian points noted. Begin with points on the bladder meridian, working from the top to the bottom. Continue the same procedure for point work shown on the liver, spleen, gall bladder and stomach meridians. Hold each point for three to five seconds. Stimulate the meridian points two times on both sides of your horse. Hold reactive points for ten to fifteen seconds. Typical reactions include rear leg lifting, muscle spasms, avoidance and weight shifting.

Stretches

Perform the buttocks, hip flexion/stifle extension, and rear leg dance stretches.

Frequency

Perform this acupressure treatment every other day for seven to ten days, or until the condition subsides. Perform stretches on the days between the acupressure treatment.

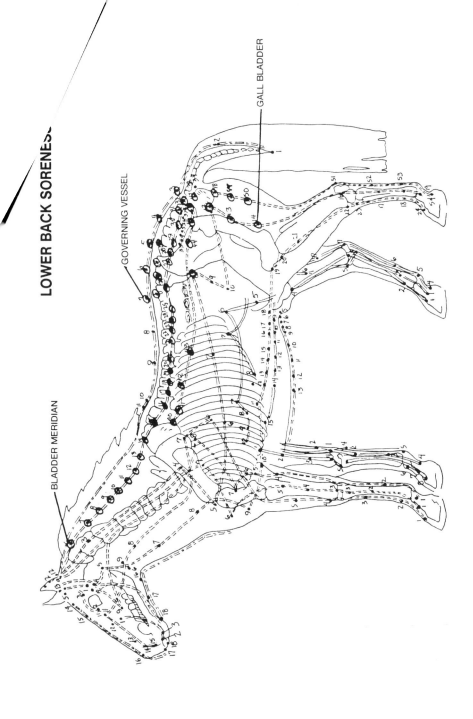

GALL BLADDER

GOVERNING VESSEL

BLADDER MERIDIAN

LOWER BACK SORENESS

Shows Up As:
- Stiff back movements
- Lack of loin flexibility
- See-saw appearance at the canter
- Formation of a hunter's bump

Refer to drawing on opposite page for points to be worked.

Procedure

This common equine ailment can be relieved by working points along the bladder, gall bladder and governing vessel meridians. Begin with the bladder meridian, stimulating the points illustrated for three to five seconds. Repeat work on these points. Work the points on the gall bladder and governing vessel meridians two times, holding for three to five seconds. Repeat the full treatment on the opposite side of your horse. Reactive points on any of the meridians should be held for ten to fifteen seconds or until a release of tension is felt. This ailment often produces reactions such as muscle spasms, rear leg extensions, tail crooking and rear leg lifts. Close your horse as previously described.

Stretches

Perform all of the rear leg stretches, the back stretches and the neck stretches. Repeat stretches two times.

Frequency

Perform this acupressure treatment and these stretches every other day for ten days or until the condition subsides. Do the acupressure treatment on one day and the stretches on the alternate day.

COLIC - PREVENTIVE

GOVERNING VESSEL MERIDIAN

STOMACH MERIDIAN

LIVER MERIDIAN

LARGE INTESTINE MERIDIAN

GALL BLADDER MERIDIAN

GOVERNING VESSEL MERIDIAN

COLIC - PREVENTIVE TREATMENT

This colic treatment is to be used exclusively in a preventive mode. That is, if your horse has a tendency to colic, this treatment can help to minimize or alleviate its colicing.

Note: Call your veterinarian immediately if your horse is showing colic symptoms.

Refer to drawing on opposite page for points to be worked.

Procedure

To help in preventing or reducing the frequency of colic in your horse, stimulate the noted points. After opening your horse, stimulate the stomach meridian points for three to five seconds. Repeat work on these points. Next stimulate the two governing vessel meridian points, holding each for three to five seconds. Repeat work on these points. Next work the gall bladder meridian points, holding each for three to five seconds. Repeat work on these points. Work the liver meridian points, again hold each for three to five seconds and repeat the work. Finally, stimulate the points noted on the face, hold each for three to five seconds. Hold reactive points on any of the meridians for ten to fifteen seconds, or until a release of tension is felt. Repeat this procedure on the other side of your horse. Close your horse as previously described. Typical reactions include an increase in gastrointestinal activity and elimination.

Stretches

None.

Frequency

Administer this acupressure treatment two times per week for the first two weeks, administer once per week thereafter.

FOUNDER

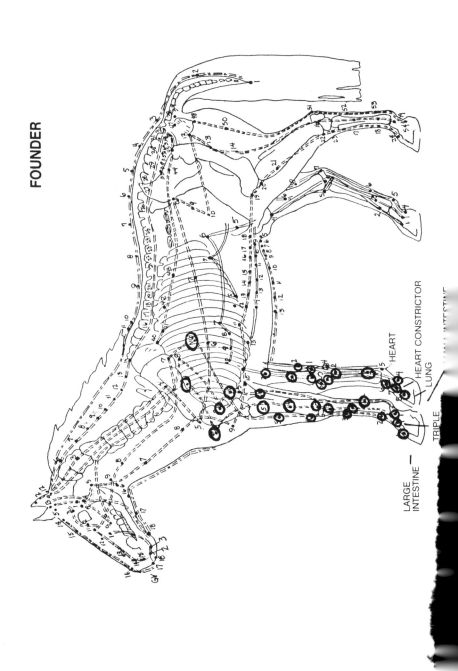

LARGE INTESTINE

TRIPLE

HEART CONSTRICTOR

LUNG

HEART

This treatment is to be used as a supplement to conventional veterinary and or farrier treatment.

Shows Up As:
- Generally front leg lameness
- Short gait and tentative foot placement
- 3-legged lameness

Refer to drawing on opposite page for points to be worked.

Procedure

To offer a measure of pain relief and improve circulation, work the large intestine, lung, triple heater, heart constrictor, small intestine and heart meridians. Begin point work at the uppermost point of each meridian noted on the opposite page. Work each meridian line downward to its terminating point. Hold each point for three to five seconds. Stimulate the meridian points twice on each front leg of your horse. Concentrate work on and around the fetlock and coronet band of each leg. Hold reactive points for ten to fifteen seconds. Typical reactions include, weight shifting, muscle spasms and avoidance.

Stretches

Triceps muscle stretch.

Frequency

Administer this acupressure treatment and stretch every other day until symptoms reside.

BIBLIOGRAPHY

1. Chinese Acupuncture, 5,000 Year Old Oriental Art of Healing, By: The International Veterinary Acupuncture Society.

2. The Complete Book of Shiatsu Therapy, By: Tory Namokoshi, Japan Publications, Inc., New York and Tokyo, 1981.

3. An Introduction to Acupuncture for Animals, By: Sheldon Altman, D.V.M., Chen's Corporation, Monteray Park, California, 1981.

4. Chinese Acupuncture Prescriptions of Horse, By: H. Grady Young, D.V.M., Oriental Veterinary Acupuncture Specialitics, Thomasville, Georgia.

5. Atlas of Veterinary Acupuncture Charts, By: H. Grady Young, D.V.M., Oriental Veterinary Acupuncture Specialities, Thomasville, Georgia 1983.

6. Amma, The Ancient Art of Oriental Healing, By: Tina Sohn, Healing Arts Press, Rochester, Vermont 1988.

7. The Web That Has No Weaver, Understanding Chinese Medicine, By: Ted Kaptchuk, O.M.D., Congdon & Weed, Inc., New York, N.Y., 1983.

8. Acupressure for Common Ailments, By: Chris Jarmey and John Tindall, Simon & Schuster Inc., New York, N.Y. 1991.

9. Tsubo Vital Points for Oriental Therapy, By: Katsusuke Serizawa, Japan Publications Inc., Tokyo & New York, 1976.

10. Zen Shiatsu, How to Harmonize Yin & Yang for Better Health, By: Shizuto Masunaga with Wataru Ohashi, Japan Publications Inc., Tokyo & New York, 1977.

Order Form

Please send me _____ copy/copies of **Equine Acupressure Treatment Workbook** @ $20.00 plus $.74 tax per book.

Please send me _____ copy/copies of the **12x18 Laminated Equine Stretch Poster** @ $15.50 plus $.59 tax per poster.

Please send me _____ copy/copies of the **12x18 Laminated Equine Meridian Chart** @ $15.50 plus $.59 tax per chart.

Please send me _____ copy/copies of the **Canine Acupressure Treatment Workbook** @ $18.50 plus $.70 tax per book.

Tax for CO residents only.

Shipping and Handling

1-5 books $3.00 per book
1-3 charts or posters $3.50
3-5 charts or posters $4.50
5-7 charts or posters $5.50

Books _____

Posters _____

Charts _____

Tax _____

Shipping/Handling _____

TOTAL FOR ORDER _____

Payment and Shipping Information

Name: _____

Address: _____

City/State: _____

Zip Code: _____ Phone: _____

MC/
Visa # _____   Exp.
Date _____

Signature: _____

Please mail order form with payment to:
Equine Acupressure, Inc.
P.O. Box 123 • Parker, CO 80134
call orders to: 303-841-7211 • fax orders to: 303-841-6939
E-mail equineacup@earthlink.net

**CLINICS AND SEMINARS AVAILABLE
CALL FOR INFORMATION**